THE BOY BORN BLUE

A story of a CHD Superhero

Written by Lena Hanna

Illustrated by Daniel Naranjo

Copyright © 2021 by Lena Hanna
ISBN: 978-1-7364988-0-4 (Paperback)
ISBN: 978-1-7364988-2-8 (Ebook)
ISBN: 978-1-7364988-1-1 (Hardcover)

This book was created especially for my son,
Decklan -
You are my hero, and I am so proud of you.
Always remember that you are a warrior and
have all the inner strength you will ever need.

To my husband -

I could not have gotten through this without you.
My world is better with you.

To my daughter -

You inspire me every day. You are
precious, amazing, and so loved.

To all the CHD warriors around the world-
You are a true inspiration to us all.

This book belongs to:

_____

(Print your superhero name)

One morning in June, a boy named Decklan was born. Despite their excitement, his parents' hearts were torn. They never got the chance to meet him on that magical day. When doctors saw their baby boy, they quickly whisked him away.

When he was born, Decklan's hands and feet were tinted a shade of royal blue. After they tested him that day, doctors confirmed what they already knew. For some reason, his heart was designed with four different flaws. This defect, named Tetralogy of Fallot, has no known cause.

"We must fully repair your son's heart within the next month or two," doctors warned his parents as they all looked over the boy born blue. "His severe defect causes low oxygen, which changes his hue. We're not exactly sure when his levels will get too low. But until it gets too risky, we'd like to see him grow."

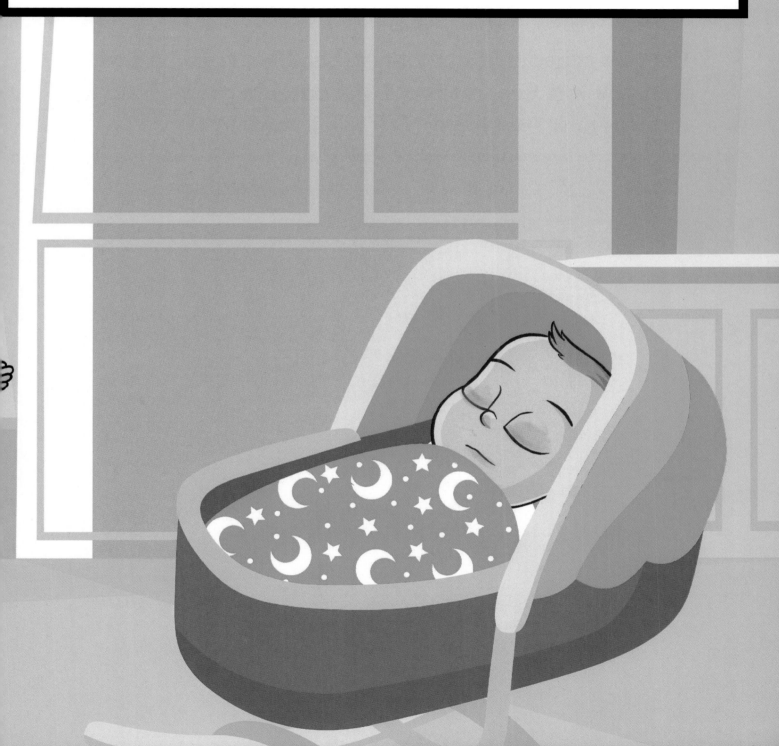

Once Decklan went home, his oxygen was monitored morning and night. Though his parents were filled with fear, the boy born blue fought with all his might. Even as his oxygen decreased, his spirit was light. Decklan's happiness remained, and his first smile shined so bright.

Doctors scheduled his walnut-sized heart to be fixed when he was five weeks old. His parents grew afraid of exactly how Decklan's story would unfold.

Surgery day came, and the boy born blue was set to be remade. Even as the doctors wheeled him away, he remained unafraid. Doctors stopped his heart and hooked him up to a huge machine so they could fix all his flaws. They put a patch on a hole and fixed some of the parts in his heart that had formed too small.

Doctors said at last, "The surgery was a success! He's doing all right, but this caused his body some stress. You'll be permitted to see him soon. Just prepare yourselves before you do."

"Your son should be released in a week to finish his recovery at home. At the moment, Decklan is on life support until he can breathe on his own."

Decklan's parents were so excited to see him, though nothing could ever prepare them for that day. They knew deep down in their hearts that no matter what, their boy born blue would ultimately make it through.

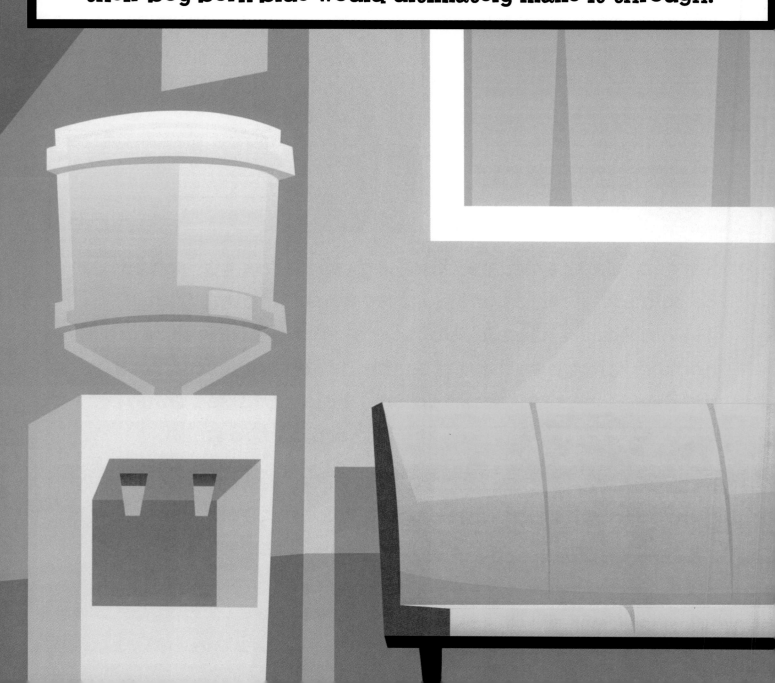

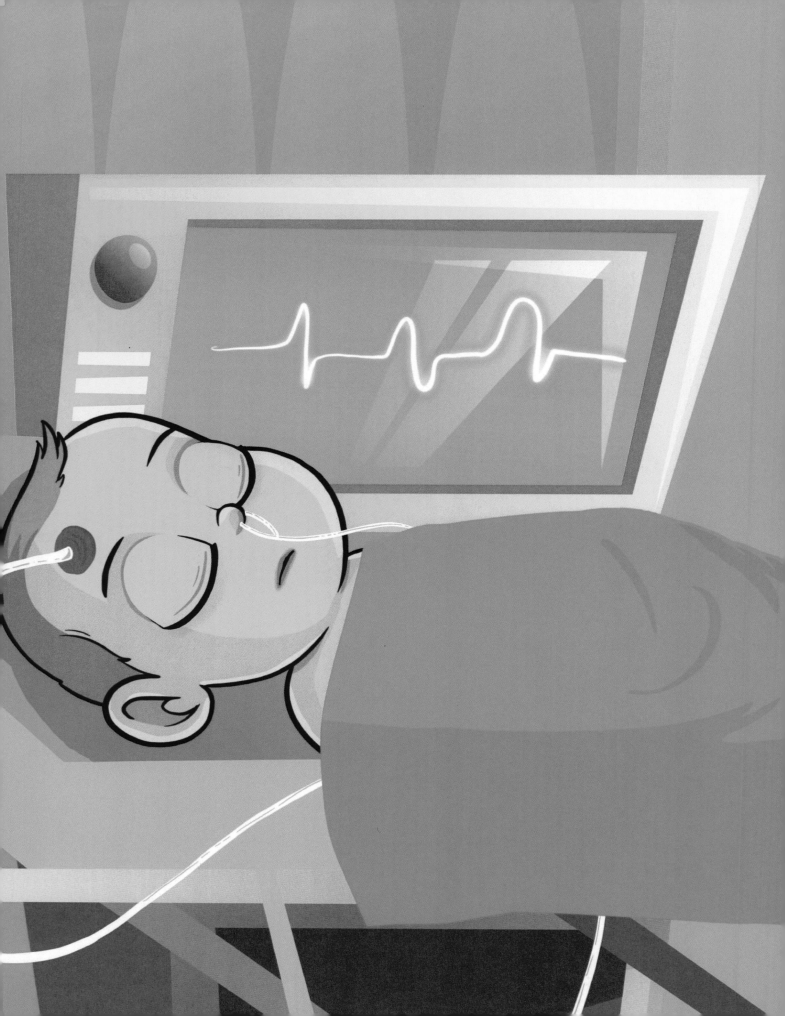

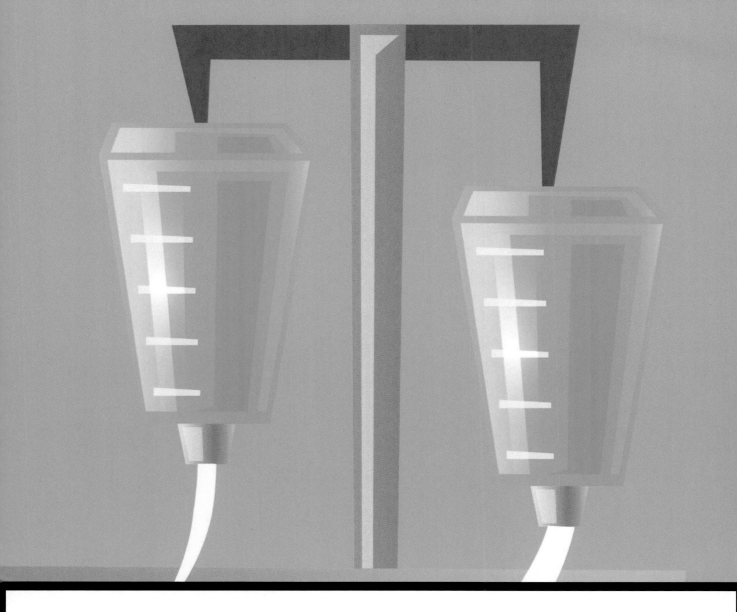

As they walked into his room, he looked so little in the middle of the hospital bed. They barely recognized him as bandages, wires, and tubes almost covered his face and head. Medicine kept him asleep and his body at full rest. He had a bandage that ran down the middle of his chest.

Their own hearts broke in half, looking at their boy born blue. They could not imagine the pain he was going through.

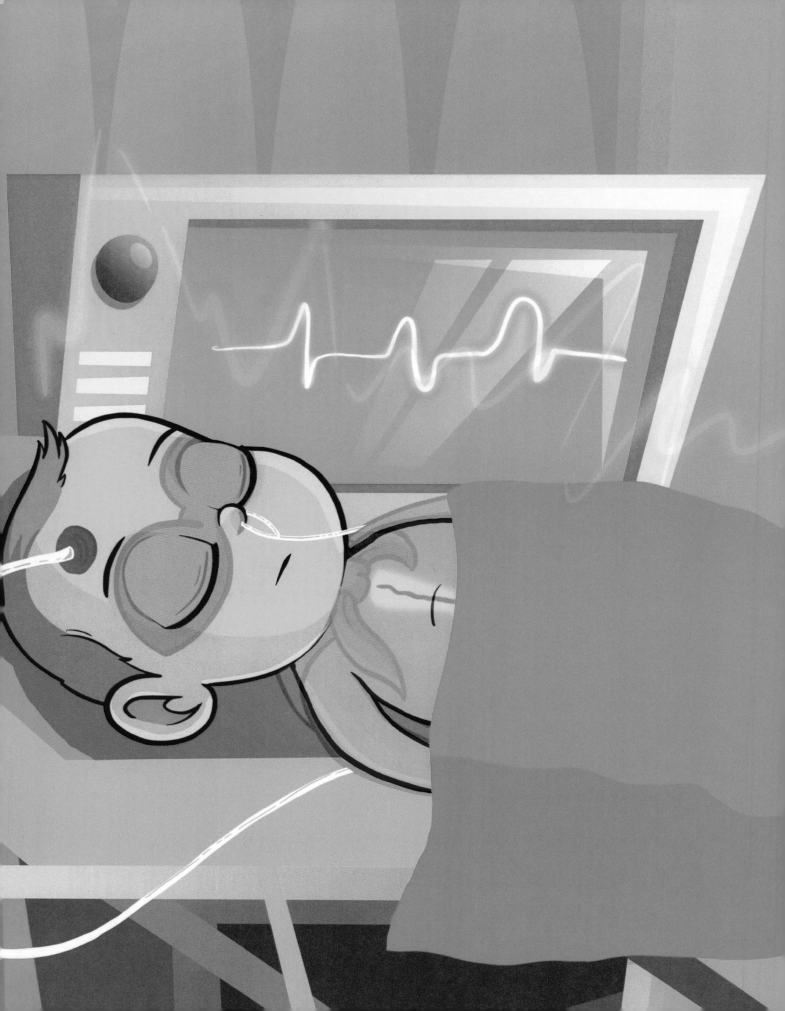

Doctors grew concerned when his recovery was not going as scheduled. Decklan still could not breathe on his own, and life support remained essential. Doctors told his parents that his lungs had started to fail. He had to stay for a week or two for extended care.

Although it seemed that no progress was being made, he was transforming into a superhero. Since birth, he always had to be so tough and brave. But it will be from this strength that he would be saved.

When Decklan woke up, his eyes opened wide. His parents were standing there by his side. He gave them a smile, and it shined so bright. His parents knew he would endure this fight.

For the next few days, he continued to drift in and out of sleep and fought hard to breathe without assistance. Decklan was so tired from the medication that kept his body still and in perfect healing position. Eventually, doctors were ready to remove his life support. His parents had hope when doctors gave him a lovely daily report.

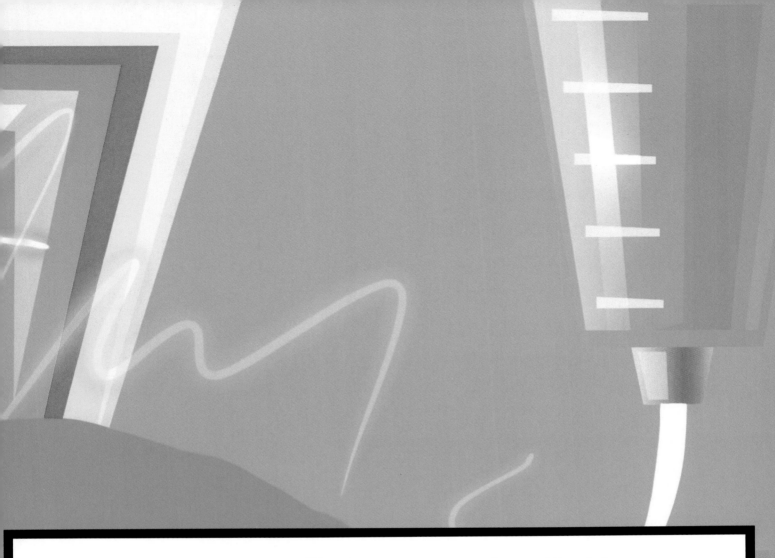

Decklan had to get off all the medication that he was put on. It was at that time that all the hope his parents had acquired was gone. As he awakened more each day, a new issue arose. Doctors grew worried and knew his discharge would be postponed.

Suddenly, Decklan stopped moving his face as he laid in the bed. He was in a full daze, and his glassy eyes just looked straight ahead. His parents brought him a few toys to get his attention. But he did not respond or change his facial expression.

Doctors broke the news to Decklan's parents of some possible and additional flaws. "He might have suffered severe damage from the amount of time his heart was put on pause. He will have to stay in the hospital until we completely figure out the cause."

Doctors had to start testing the boy born blue once again. They had to figure out if something happened with his brain. For days, he had tons of wires attached to his head covered up by a thin white hat. Yet, Decklan was not bothered and knew that it was just another thing to combat.

Days later, doctors informed his parents about the insight they gained. "We now have ruled out any significant problems with Decklan's brain. It may be an effect from the medication he got for pain. It's going to be a long road for you, but he can go home in a day or two."

Doctors soon removed the large, white bandage down his chest that covered his scar. The wound looked like an exclamation point and proved he was a superstar.

He entered the hospital as the boy born blue and left a true fighter. He showed everyone that he was nothing but an actual survivor.

Decklan got through all the struggles that came his way. His pure fearlessness carried him through every day. He became a true warrior by fighting through it all. He rose above every challenge and after every fall.

There are more surgeries to come and a lifetime of care. But it will never be more than the boy born blue can bear. He has an endless supply of strength and massive amount of courage. Decklan is a superhero, a fighter, and was born to flourish.

His smile is so bright that it could shine through any gloomy cloud. After all of this, he is still the happiest boy around. His smile can make the saddest people smile too. He is a superhero all the way through.

Decklan has taught his parents so much they never knew. Now, the boy born blue wants to spread the message to you . . .

There will be times when life seems unfair,

but do not be afraid or despair.

Be a fighter and always remember,

struggles build your strength and make you better.

When you face challenges and never surrender,

you can be your own superhero forever!

ABOUT THE AUTHOR

Lena Hanna was born and raised on Long Island, NY and has lived there most of her life. She attended Baruch College, City University of New York, where she attained a degree in accounting and graduated magna cum laude. She has worked as an accountant since 2005. She enjoys her life with her husband and two children.

It was the birth of her son, Decklan, that inspired her to publish a children's book. He was born with a critical congenital heart defect and underwent open heart surgery at just five weeks old. The difficulties that her son and her family faced due to his condition had a profound effect on her. Lena set out to spread awareness on congenital heart defects.

Her book, The Boy Born Blue: The Story of a CHD Superhero, follows the beginning of Decklan's journey. Lena hopes the story of her son's surgery will be inspirational and offer hope to all children, while also teaching them to fight against adversity.
In the future, Lena's greatest hope is for a long, healthy life for her son and to see both her children thrive and prosper. She is currently writing a second children's book detailing her daughter's struggles with the transition of being an only child to becoming a sister of a child with a critical illness.

Website: www.lenahanna.com
Instagram: @lenanhanna / Facebook: @lenanhanna
Email: lena@lenahanna.com

Made in the USA
Columbia, SC
23 October 2022